Art by

lavish

www.lavish-art.co.uk

Published in Great Britain and Ireland in 2006 by Imagineire Limited,
3300 Lake Drive, Citywest Business Campus, Dublin 24, Ireland.

ISBN 10: 1-904725-47-3
ISBN 13: 978-1-904725-47-3

This volume is dedicated...

To all our lovely owners
Who think that we can't speak
Who think we only bark and growl
Miaow, or squawk, or squeak

We do, indeed, have voices
We use them all the time
At the legendary Pet Poets Club
The home of rhythm and rhyme

Signed: *The Pet Poets Club*

Rural Somerset - June 1976

The paperboy pedalled a little faster as he realised his daily round was almost over. Although still dark, the chatter of the birds told him that daybreak wasn't far away.

He pushed his last paper through the letterbox and walked back to his bicycle.

It was then that he saw it, coming towards him up the lane. Unclear at first, he was soon able to discern the unmistakable form of a large dog: a black Labrador.

Slowly, the dog walked up to the paperboy and sat down. It was then that the boy saw the thing in the dog's mouth, a thing that the dog seemed to be inviting him to take.

"What have you got there, then? Is that for me?" the boy enquired.

He bent down and took the object from the dog's mouth - an unmarked tape cassette. The boy turned it over for some sign of what might be on it but there was none.

With his package delivered, the dog nonchalantly turned around and trotted off back down the lane in the direction it had come from.

The boy jumped onto his bike and pedalled home as quickly as he could. As soon as he arrived, he rushed upstairs to his bedroom and thrust the cassette into his tape player.

He pressed "Play".

At first he heard nothing. Then he heard a dog barking. The bark wasn't like old man Puckett's dog next door, loud and aggressive. It sounded somehow rhythmic. Next on the tape was the sound of a cat, once again with that same rhythmic feel. There then followed a whole variety of animal noises - horsey sounds, squawky birds, funny little squeaking tunes, weird bubbling and lots more cats and dogs.

His head whirled. What was this strange collection of sounds? Who had recorded this tape? And why had a big black Labrador delivered it to him at 6.45 in the morning?

It would be almost 25 years, before Marc Todd (no longer a paperboy) would discover the answers, but when he did he could hardly believe what it was that he had found!

I really find it tiring
That people think I'm thick
And crave to pass the time of day
Playing "Catch-It" with a stick

I don't want to go "walkies"
When I'd rather have a nap
When will I ever get some peace?
I'm not a happy chap

I do not like cold water
So I don't react with glee
When expected to go in and fetch
A frisbee from the chilly sea

"He's worn me out today," they say
Well stuff this for a lark!
I didn't ask to chase a ball
Around a freezing park!

I have a cosy basket
Beside a radiator
So why this urge to go outside?
Can it not be left till later?

... Like later in the year
When the sun is nice and warm?
I won't mind going outside then
When I'll be on better form

But today outside it's snowing
And I hope they're not inspired
To drag me out, can they not see?
I'm really quite dog tired

Dog tired

ZZZZZZZZZZ

ZZZZZZZZ

ZZZZZZ

ZZZZZZZ

THE CASE OF
THE CURIOUS KITTEN

Why have I got whiskers
Poking out my face?

These sharp little claws on all four paws
Seem very out of place

My tail is long but surely wrong
Though it's very good to chase

I'm very weird and a little dog-eared
I'm an all-round curious case!

Lettuce give thanks
(a rabbit's prayer)

Let us give thanks for the lettuce
'Tis truly a gift from above
Nature's greatest creation, divine inspiration
A life full of lettuce is a life filled with love

How I worship the heavenly Ice-Berg
How I treasure the sweet Little-Gem
These miracles of flavour, all my life may I savour
Every day I shall give praise for them

Hallelujah, Radicchio and Rocket
Thee bringers of passion and flair
May I thrive on thy goodness till death doth me take
Lord of lettuce, please hear my prayer

Ah… lettuce

I remember, but I'm not sure what!

I remember I'm a goldfish
And that's about the lot
I know I swim in water
But water... hmmm... is what?

I think I live inside a bowl
I've forgotten how I know
Somebody must have told me
A long, long time ago

I'm sure I'm here all on my own
Of that I am fairly clear
"Oh, good morning George, nice day for it"
I'd forgotten he was here

BAD SPORTS

IN THE AVIARY

I've been trying to set up a bird band
Without much success to report
I'd have thought that this flock would have wanted to rock
But the only thing that rocks them is sport

There's a budgie named Dennis who loves table tennis
And he's really got quite a fine voice
But he'd rather play ping-pong than join in a sing song
If you ask me a very poor choice

There's a parrot called Sooty who'd rather play footie
Than pluck a few chords on guitar
If he'd rather play ball than answer my call
Then, with him, I shan't get very far

There's a Welsh mynah bird, name of Gareth
And a mynah sounds great in choir
But that miserable bugger would rather play rugger
Things are starting to look pretty dire

There's a sweet humming bird who's called Florence
With rhythm, she really is brimming
And a bird that likes humming should really love drumming
But she'd rather be synchronised swimming

Now Tom is a yellow canary
Who'd look great strumming hard on a bass
But he much prefers bowling to rockin' and rollin'
So it's now time to start saving face

I've decided I'm going to go solo
I'm making an artistic stand
It's fine that they're sporting, but they should be supporting
Our aviary's fledgling bird band

Round and round and round and round
Around I went and guess what I found?
If you don't keep running, you're sure to fail
And that's the beginning of this hamster's tale

Scurry, scurry, quickly, scurry
Whatever you do, always do it in a hurry
Only the fastest are sure to prevail
As we come to the middle of this hamster's tale

Five tiny twitching balls of fluff
The hours in a day are never enough
With so many depending, your problems soon pale
That's the end of the middle of this hamster's tale

Sleeping so snug in your own sleepy ball
The need to go slow, slowly comes to us all
Life should be a breeze, not a gust or a gale
And now we've reached the end of this hamster's tale

HAMSTERSMITH APOLLO
DIRECT FROM THE EXERCISE BALL
A PERFORMANCE IN FOUR PARTS
A HAMSTER'S TALE
A REFLECTION ON LIFE FROM A GIANT OF THE STAGE
"HAROLD THE HAMSTER IS QUITE OUTSTANDING"
"I CRIED, I LAUGHED, I CRIED AGAIN. WHAT EMOTION!"
"A TRIUMPH!"
- PLUS -
THRILL AT THE ANTICS OF
GORDON THE GALLOPING GERBIL

FIFI

The showbiz Chihuahua

I love looking down on my fellow pups
You can't beat the feeling of power
Carried aloft in a movie star's bag
I'm Fifi the showbiz Chihuahua

Paris, London, New York or Rome
It's the red-carpet treatment for me
Adorned head to toe in a sparkly pink bow
I'm a fashion accessory

My peers all think that I'm silly
But I get into everywhere free
Invited by name and showered with fame
I'm canine glitterati

Did you know I'm worth a mint?

I bet you would never have guessed

Ten thousand quid at the very last count

Now admit it, you're really impressed

Some lesser fish think it's vulgar

To be worth so much lurvely cash

But bugger to them, if they want to be poor

What is wrong with a fish being flash?

A NOT-SO-KOI CARP

The quickest way

Have you ever wondered
Just how you're going to go?
I guess most of us, if given the choice
Would rather never know

But if you are a thinker
Who dwells in morbid climes
Then spare a thought for us poor cats
Who almost die nine times!

So many different pathways
To the cattery in the sky
So paws for thought, while I think
Of the quickest **nine** ways to nearly die

Stuck up a tree in a hurricane when the fire brigade's on strike
Sneaking in the kennel next door and weeing on their pet dog Spike
Hiding in the kitchen on Christmas Day and eating half the turkey
Using the sofa as a scratching post, could turn your future rather murky
Impersonating cat's-eyes in the middle of the road
Leaving lots of "little messages" in the family's precious abode
Leaving a bird on the doorstep if that bird is the pet canary
Walking barefoot on a hot tin roof is also pretty scary

But the quickest way is to think all day
How you'll end up six feet under
So live each day as if it's your last
And enjoy a life of wonder!

Rabbit, rabbit, rabbit

I have to say I'm hopping mad
It really isn't funny
Living in the very same hutch
As a non-stop talking bunny

Rabbit, rabbit, rabbit
That's all one ever hears
I wish I had some cotton wool
To stuff inside my ears

It's "He said this, and she said that"
Every hour of the day
If I only had a passport
I'd love to fly away

I'd jet off to an island
Somewhere without any noise
And spend my days in blissful peace
Eating carrots with the boys

But I know it's just a daydream
And I should get in the habit
Of joining in and getting used
To rabbit, rabbit, rabbit

I'm sticking where I am

"Branch out, young man, and see the world"

Was what my parents said

But I didn't twig which world they meant

So I munched a leaf instead

"We know we would, if we were you"

They chorused every day

But I didn't twig, I thought that wood

Was what I looked like anyway

"Don't be a stick-in-the-mud forever

There's so much to do and see"

But they didn't twig that being stuck

At being a stick was just fine by me

Owl very strange

Tuh-wit, tuh-woo

It's strange but it's true

And you'll really gasp when I tell it…

… Tuh-wit, tuh-woo

In place of a poo…

I regurgitate a pellet!

Poetry in *slow* motion

I like to take things slowly...

... Is there any better way?

If you take everything slow

Then you'll always know...

... you'll have plenty to do the **next** day

Recollections of a (*retired*) Dorset cat-burglar

Ooh-aarr me boy, I tells you wot
These cat-flap things be murder
They really don't do anything
To 'elp an old cat-burglar

You need a special magnet thing
Or you can't get in an' out
I s'pose they must have gotten wind
That burglars be about

In the old days it were easy
Back doors they'd never close
You'd slither in without a sound
And simply follow yer nose

Then tiptoe to the kitchen
And see what be in the bowl
All me life I've dined on the very best
And all of it I've stole

To a cat like me, it's in the blood
Though some say I'm a sinner
To 'elp meself, till I've 'ad my fill
Of someone else's dinner

The pony quartet

The Sloaney Pony

Oh isn't it simply super?
It's such a spiffing day
There are so many lovely ponies here
Who have all come out to play

It's the cream of pony society
A place where one has to be seen
It's so awfully posh, that even the nosh
Would be fit for a show jumping queen

There are oodles of dishy chaps here
That are catching the eye of this filly
But I'm much too embarrassed to make the first move
Oh, I'm just such a shy silly-billy

I think I'll just stay here and mingle
There are so many things to enjoy
And perhaps the next pony who speaks to me
Will be a nice, sloaney pony boy

The Moany Pony

I really don't know why she thinks
I find gymkhanas fun
Puffing around with a lump on my back
She must weigh half a tonne

The crowd are much too noisy
With all those "Oohs" and "Aahhs"
And it isn't her that feels the pain
When we smack into those bars

The ground's too hard, the slope's too steep
The fences much too high
How on earth does she think I'll get over them?
Perhaps she thinks I can fly!

No... I've had enough of this silly event
And although I shouldn't oughta
I'll gonna pull up at the very next jump
And pitch her right into the water!

the gymkhana suite

The Testeroni Pony

Ciao, beautiful pony ladeez
Zis is your lucky day
The Testeroni pony has arrived in the ring
To carry your virtue away

With zis fiesty Italian stallion
Your heart will set forth on a foray
That is certain to end in the ride of your life
With this prince of equine amore

My dressage is passion in motion
As I strut, wiggle, canter and tease
My nostrils are flared, my muscles are pumped,
So come along all you ladeez

You should really not try to fight it
Let me ignite your feminine fire
Take a roll in the mud with zis high-jumping stud
And give in to your pony desire

The Phoney Pony

I'm by far the fastest pony here
I can jump the highest too
I'm tall and strong and my legs are long
But there's something not quite true

I'm a champion in the pony world
But the truth you've guessed, of course
I'm not a proper pony, and never have been
I'm really just a little horse!

AN INCREASINGLY
HOT DOG

I wish I had a girlfriend
Someone to share my day
But every time I sniff one out
They simply run away

Perhaps they find me ugly
Or do they think I'm smelly?
I'm getting sick of stopping in
And goggling at the telly

I really want a girlfriend
I've such a lot to give
Daily I'd make their dreams come true
If 'twas me that they were with

My other pals are sorted
They've always got a bitch
Even Reg the whippet's got a squeeze
Even with that funny twitch!

I need a bloody girlfriend!
What do I have to do!
I'm young, I'm fit, and I've got a job
Well... two of those are true

Nookie's all I think about!
Some say it's overrated
I'd love to find out for myself
Oh god, I'm so frustrated!

I'm desperate for a lover!
I've got to find one now!
And I don't care if I have to beg
Or stand on my head and howl!

But I must be calm and wait my time
One day I'll strike it lucky
And believe you me, that day will be
Really, really mucky!

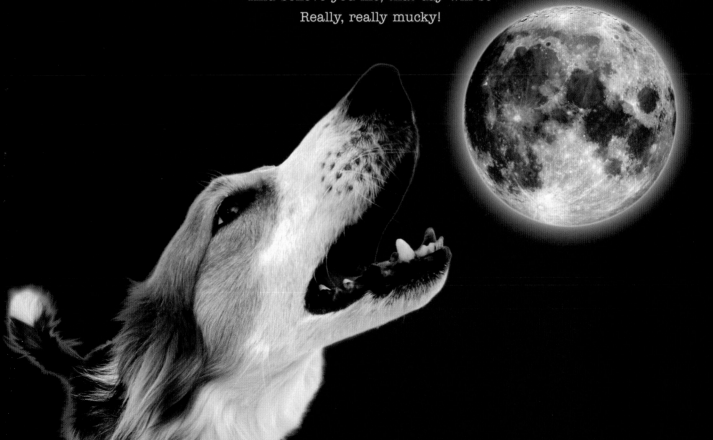

Hear me brothers, one and all
The time has come to act
No more shall we be put upon
Come join me in a pact

Our fat cat boss exploits us all
But brothers, we have rights
We must stand strong and be prepared
For many long cat fights

For far too long we've toiled hard
While he collects the money
We catch his birds, we chase his mice
And he just thinks it's funny

So join with me and fight for right
Let's hear it for the cause
I say we hold a wild-cat strike
Let's have a show of paws

It's time to bring the fat cat down
We'll start a revolution
And march toward our chosen goal
Of wealth redistribution

The fur will fly, the claws will out
But brothers we will win
Let's cut the feed to feline greed
And make that fat cat thin!

Who's a pretty boy, then?

Who's a pretty boy, then?
I'm sure it isn't you
We all know boys aren't pretty
Pretty's what girls do

Who's a pretty boy, then?
I know it isn't me
Parrots don't look pretty
We just look feathery

Who's a pretty boy, then?
Perhaps it's this chap here?
But he's just made of plastic
And rather plain, I fear

Who's a pretty boy, then?
I'll never get to know, and so...
... I wish I could stop saying it
But they're the only words I know!

What you lookin' at, then?

Do yer fancy 'avin' a go?

Be quiet, Chas, you're such a yob

He only said "Hello"

Are you lookin' at my bird?

Did you spill my beer?

If you're not polite, I'll call it a night

And jolly well leave you here

Come an' 'ave a go if you think yer hard enough?

You want a bit of bovver?

That's it, goodbye, I've had enough

I'm going back to Mother!

Oh Treacle, please don't leave me 'ere,

Come on, gizza snog!

Too late, I'm off, and I won't be back

You're an uncouth dirty dog

But you're my little princess

You've always blimmin' been

But darling... princess isn't good enough

I want to be the queen!

the Ballad of Chas and camilla

Chas

Camilla

I wish the blend would end

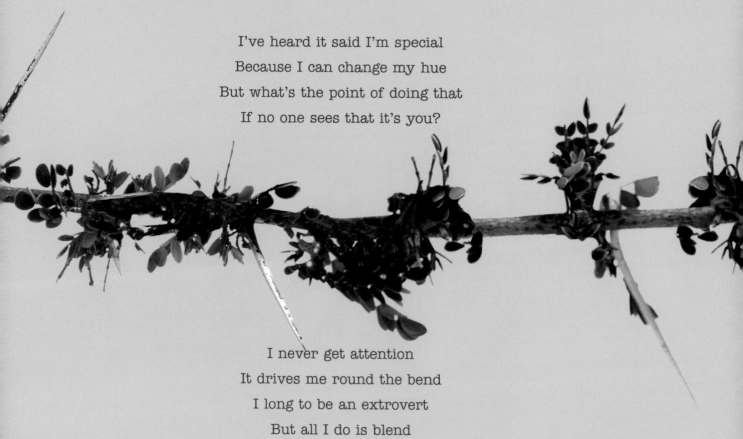

I'm sick and tired of blending in
Oh why can't I stand out?
If I want to get myself noticed
I have to really shout

I've heard it said I'm special
Because I can change my hue
But what's the point of doing that
If no one sees that it's you?

I never get attention
It drives me round the bend
I long to be an extrovert
But all I do is blend

The blend

a mouse... with a

My life is such a headache
My finances are on the skids
Well, wouldn't yours, if you had to feed
Twenty-seven kids?

My wife is *always* pregnant
It's really not that nice
Having to share the marital home
With so many baby mice

I really should be honoured
That my genes are so prolific
"What's that, my dear? You're pregnant again?
Well, that is just terrific!"

Another bunch of mouths to feed
Does she think I'm made of money?
I'm getting far too old for this
It really isn't funny

I need to put an end to this
My wallet just can't cope
Just me and the wife, and some time on our own...
Well, you can always live in hope!

Very full house

I remember the first time I saw her
The day she came into my life
Although I was young, I knew she was the one
And swore some day I'd make her my wife

She sent my young heart all a-flutter
This beautiful bird without par
She was silent and still, but I felt such a thrill
She enraptured this budgerigar

She put such a spring in this young budgie's step
And I knew that she felt the same way
Her spring, I could see, sent a message to me
It said, "Why don't you kiss me today?"

In a blink I was right up beside her
This exotic and glamorous thing
A shy little peck, in the small of her neck...
And the world surely heard my heart sing!

Over and over I kissed her
My glorious and glossy pink lover
And with each kiss I'd rain, she'd spring straight up again
And offer her face for another

I just knew that I had to go further
As my passion continued to swell
I pecked faster and harder, inflamed in my ardour
I was certainly ringing her bell!

A match in he

made...

…aven

And then, all too soon, it was over
My head felt as light as a feather
As she stood there so still, I could feel my heart fill
With a love that would last us forever

We have never spent even one day apart
As year after year has flown by
We're perfect together, we're two of a kind
My beautiful soul mate and I

She looks just the same as the first day we met
When that seed in my heart was first planted
Only one little thing, a kink in her spring
Stops me thinking she must be enchanted

But it's me that's enchanted, and always will be
Forever, my love has stayed true
With her on my perch, I've had no need to search…
… out the pleasures of budgie birds new

Oh what a life we have shared, she and I
Every moment a mountain of pleasure
And though fate has decreed that no heir shall I breed
I've already discovered my treasure

But I think, very soon, I may drop off my perch
I'm nearing the end of my age
But my death I shan't fear, as I'll soon be back here
Because heaven is here with her… in this cage

love
Missy
x

Nine out of ten ad directors
Preferred me as their feline star
I was Missy the model stunt cat
A professional puss without par

I could sit, or run, or jump or sleep
Whatever they needed, I'd do it
My face was known across the land
But one day I really blew it!

I was doing an ad for coal fires
It starred me, and a dog, and a mouse
We all took our places with our best friendly faces
Three lovey pets in a warm toasty house

But when I get hot, I get hungry
The temptation became all too real
In a moment of madness, I was consumed by badness
And my co-star became my next meal

Luckily the crew didn't see me
They all thought the mouse ran away
Nine out of ten times I wouldn't have done it
And I live with the guilt to this day

Sadly I was seen by someone
And that angry someone was Rover
As I cowered in fear, he bit off my ear
And my modelling days are now over!

a very *long* day!

I've a bit of a problem, though I'm sure nothing's wrong

It's just all of my poos are quite stupidly... long!

I really go quite red when all the other goldfish scoff

So I swim at speed around the tank, to try and knock it off

I'm always very conscious of this yucky thing I dangle

I need to watch out what's below in case I get a tangle

Seems the more that I worry, the longer it gets

And now one of the lads has begun taking bets

It's at fifteen to one that it stays there all day

I certainly hope not as it's starting to sway!

But then just as I worry it might never unravel

Off it drops suddenly... and gets lost in the gravel

I'm lost for words, what can I say?
I can't believe I've won today
If I thought that these heights I would ever reach
I'd have written a proper acceptance speech

I'd like to thank all of my family
For their love, their support, and their pedigree
To my wonderful trainer, I owe this to you
You have made all the dreams of this collie come true

My thanks go to Lassie, the star of our age
And all the great dogs who've appeared on this stage
It's for them, not for me, you should give your applause
I'm just honoured to follow in such giant paws

Your votes for my work are an honour indeed
I was humbled you named me your "Best of Breed"
I had longed for that day since a very small pup
Oh dear… sniff… please excuse me, I'm welling up

But a greater still honour you were yet to bestow
You decided to vote me your "Best in Show"
Who'd have guessed that my tale would have this way unfurled
I can now bark out loud… "I'M THE KING OF THE WORLD!"

Show me the way to go home

Eeh by gum, A'm in a mess
A've really lost me way
I don't even know me own address
This happens every day

A'm supposed to find me own way home
With me powers of detection
But there's one thing that I sorely lack...
... A've no sense of direction!

A've no idea of where I've flown
Or where I should be flying
I need a route that's set in stone
Instead of just "blue skying"

I really need to get a map
That's clear from this 'ere tome
Then never again would I get in a flap
A'd simply just find me way 'ome

Every Sunday morning
Me and the chaps have a chat
We talk about hunting, we talk about fishing
The things you'd expect from a cat

But every Sunday morning
The one thing we talk about most
It's the only thing on which we can never agree
Which is... which is the best Sunday roast

Now Oscar's a bit of a bruiser
A scrapper with very strong teeth
He loves a good chew, so it won't surprise you
To discover he favours roast beef

Babe is a bit of a grandad
And with stiffness and aches he is stricken
But he knows his own mind, and each Sunday you'll find
Him getting stuck into a chicken

Our Missy's a bit of gourmet
And there's only one meat she'll endorse
As the gravy is stirring, she's already purring
At the thought of roast lamb and mint sauce

As for me, I'm just so undecided
But choosing is half of the fun
Beef, lamb or chicken, they're all well worth picking
But I have to decide on just one

So I'm going to plump for the... chicken!
I vote it my favourite roast dinner
Whether leg, wing or breast, I think poultry's the best
And that means that chicken's the winner!

A Rat's Dilemma

When people say they've smelt a rat
I think it's downright rude
It isn't them that has to rummage
In a dustbin for their food

A pet rat's life is rather fine
And cleaner, that's for sure
As I play, and roll, and slide across
This lovely polished floor

I sleep in comfy sawdust
And dine on nuts and seeds
I really am quite pampered
And have no pressing needs

But am I being ratty?

A traitor to my kin?

Should I be down a damp, dark pipe?

Or in a smelly bin?

It's a rather big dilemma

I'm facing quite a test

A life replete with luxury?

Or slumming it with the rest?

But after much soul-searching

My doubts are now much fewer

And I'm sure I'd rather lord it here

Than paddle through a sewer

A spider inside her

I've always fancied hairy men
hairy just cannot be beaten
So I always hate that after we mate
By me they end up eaten

I suppose they know it's coming
And I hope they don't find it too scary
But perhaps I wouldn't be so inclined
If they weren't all so deliciously hairy

I've been through twenty-one so far
Another will be along very soon
He'll give me a flash of his eight hairy legs
And then this lady spider will swoon

And then it will all be over
And I'll do what tarantulas do
I'll kiss him goodnight with a venomous bite
And tuck into Dad 22

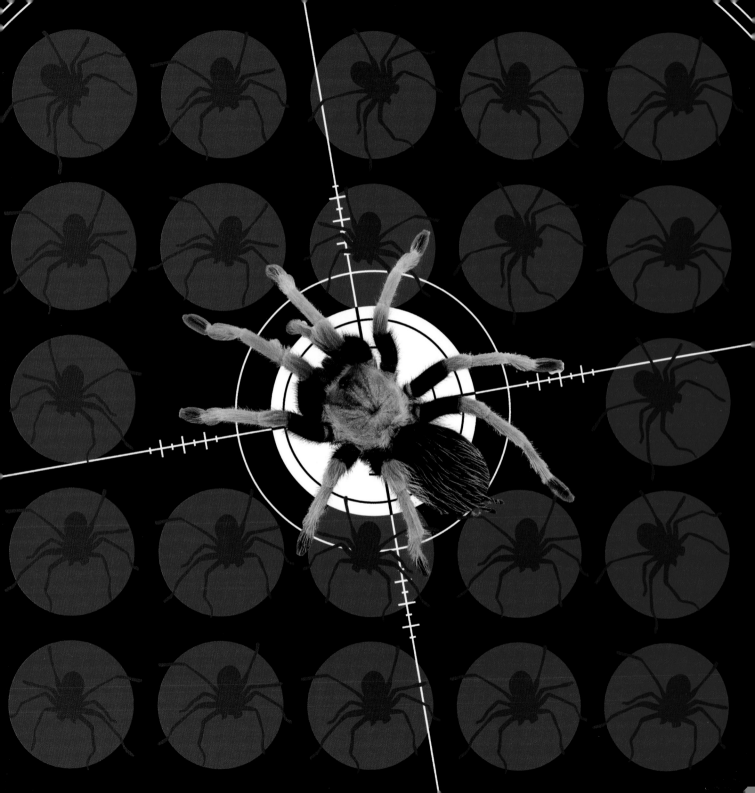

The Dogfather

If you have got a bone to pick
Then you can bring me your bone
I'm the top dog in this neighbourhood
I'm The Dogfather – Pugsy Malone

All the dogs here owe me favours
For helping sort out tricky things
I know everything happening here on my turf
I'm the one who is working the strings

If some cat on your patch is becoming a pest
I can soon make that problem be gone
All it needs is a whisper in somebody's ear
And a woof from your neighbourhood Don

I'll make others give you whatever you want
Just tell me the thing that you choose
I'll persuade them they really should do as I ask
With an offer they cannot refuse

Ronny Rottweiler is one of my mob
He's my man when the going gets ruff
My pug-mug, I know, makes me look pretty mean
But really I'm not all that tough

I just adore the feeling of power
It's a must when you're titchy like me
So I act like a gangster by mumbling my growls
And pretending I'm from Sicily

An **A to Z** of the Pet Poets Club

A is the **ART**, which a Pet Poet creates

B are the **BARDS**, which we have here in spates

C is for **CREATURES**, be they great, be they small

D is the **DREAMERS**; we're a stage for them all

E is for **ENTRY** which is free, if you're a pet

F are the **FRIENDS** – of whom so many we have met

G is for **GENUINE** – we **are** the real thing

H is our **HEADQUARTERS**, where poetry is king

I is for **INSPIRED**, which we are every day

J is for **JUMPIN'**, when we're really carried away!

K is for **KINDRED** – we're all artists together

L are the **LINES** – full of skill and endeavour

M is for **MEMORIES** unique and revealing

N is for **NARRATIVE**, overflowing with feeling

O is the **OVATION** that our poets deserve

P are the **POEMS** – full of passion and verve

Q is for **QUIET!**, during tomes of reflection

R is the **RHYME**, gently honed to perfection

S are the **SENTENCES**, brimming with style

T are the **TALES** that make all of us smile

U is for **UNDERGROUND**, and the way we will stay

V is for **VERBALISING** – it's the Pet Poets way

W is our **WHEREABOUTS** a top-secret location

X is for **XPERTS**, who have found their vocation

Y is for **YES**, these last rhymes **are** rather tricky

Z is for ????? **ZEBRA** – well, you can't be too picky!

Happy Birthday!

Happy Christmas

Cards and loads more!

Poem of the month!

THE PPC News

Check out all the latest PPC news online!

LOOK OUT FOR...

THE Pet Poets CLUB

The Dogs

Transcribed by Mare Todd

DOGS

Look out for more wise words from the Pet Poets!

THE Pet Poets CLUB

The Cats

Transcribed by Mare Todd

CATS